Copyright © 2021-All rights reserved.

No part of this publication may be reproduced, distributed, or transmitted in any form or by any means, including photocopying, recording, or other electronic or mechanical methods, without the prior written permission of the publisher, except in the case of brief quotations embodied in reviews and certain other non-commercial uses permitted by copyright law.

This Book is provided with the sole purpose of providing relevant information on a specific topic for which every reasonable effort has been made to ensure that it is both accurate and reasonable. Nevertheless, by purchasing this Book you consent to the fact that the author, as well as the publisher, are in no way experts on the topics contained herein, regardless of any claims as such that may be made within. It is recommended that you always consult a professional prior to undertaking any of the advice or techniques discussed with in.This is a legally binding declaration that is considered both valid and fair by both the Committee of Publishers Association and the American Bar Association and should be considered as legally binding within the United States.

CONTENTS

INTRODUCTION

Your body was made to be a one stop shop for everything it needs in life to be strong healthy and serve you right. Somewhere along the way, from the tie of our ancestors, our bodies started growing heavier and heavier and weaker and weaker.

What could have changed? Why is it that despite the amount of advancements that we see in science and technology, we are getting sicker than ever before? Well, it always starts with food. We are going to look at a disease that mostly goes undiagnosed but has some of the most uncomfortable symptoms. We are talking bloating constipation, rectal bleeding, chills, nausea, fever and severe abdominal pain.

Diverticulitis is a disease that starts affecting people who are 40 years and above and our aim is to provide more information in order to establish ways in which we can avoid getting this disease or in the case that we already have it, we can manage it without the discomfort that it brings.

We are not talking about a diet that you have to follow for the next 3 to 6 months. On the contrary, we are introducing a lifestyle that will not only help with diverticulitis but also in keeping your body generally healthy and strong to help you lead your best life.

This will involve you bidding goodbye some of your previous habits such as eating processed foods or fast food and other order in meals that are mostly doused with sugar, fat and salt. This eBook will help rewire your body so you are able to eat the kind of food that your body needs and you also start reaping the benefits of doing so.

Without further ado, let's jump right in!

Diverticular Disease Explained

Diverticular disease refers to three medical conditions that involve the growth of small pouches or sacs in the wall of the colon and these are diverticulosis, diverticulitis and diverticula bleeding.

- Diverticulosis

Diverticulosis is a condition that involves the formation of numerous tiny diverticula (pouches or sacs), in the lining of the bowel. These pockets are formed when there's increased pressure on the weak spots of intestinal walls that are caused by waste, gas or liquid. Diverticular can develop when you are straining when passing stool especially if you are constipated.

Diverticula mostly form in the lower portion of the colon known as the sigmoid colon as a result of it working overtime trying to push out hardened waste or eating very little food. With our diet becoming more and more fiber deficient, diverticula is becoming increasingly common. As per the latest statistics, 10 percent of the people over age 40 and 50 percent of people over age 60 have diverticulosis. But, it's important to note that most people with diverticulosis will have very few or even no symptoms.

- Diverticulitis

Diverticulitis develops as a result of diverticulosis that leads to the formation of pouches known as diverticular. Diverticulitis occurs when the diverticular become infected or inflamed resulting in extreme abdominal pain, nausea, fever and a change in bowel movement routine. Infections are caused by small pieces of waste or fecal matter getting trapped inside the small pockets of the diverticular usually due to constipation. It is also possible for ingested food to get trapped. In either case, this offers an ideal breeding ground for bacteria hence the inflammation and infection.

- Diverticulitis bleeding

These occurs when diverticulitis is not addressed or becomes severely infected to the point that the diverticular walls start bleeding. It is very painful and the main symptom is traces of blood in the stool.

Can I get Diverticulitis?

Before the twentieth century, diverticular disease was one of the rarest diseases but today, it has become really common especially in the Western world. Diverticular disease is a collection of medical conditions that affect the digestive tract with the most serious being diverticulitis.

In the United States alone, it affects approximately half of all people who are above 60 years of age and almost everyone who is 80 years and above. As we get older, the pouches in our digestive tract start becoming more and more prominent.

If you are under 40 years of age, it is very unlikely that you are going to develop diverticulosis unless your diet is very low on fiber or unless you deprive yourself nutritionally by eating way lower than the recommended intake. Diverticulosis also develops in people who do not take a high fiber diet and that is why it is very common in Western countries as the diet is not rich in fiber and not in Asia of Africa as their diet is high in fiber.

Let's go back to the very beginning!

When we look at how our ancestors lived and how strong their bodies were then we have to agree that they were definitely doing something right. We are talking about a community that was primarily hunter gatherer and survived on the game meat they hunted or if we even come back a little closer to our time, the animals that they had managed to domesticate and the plants and grains that they could gather or plant.

This is a time when there was no fast food or any food factory for that matter. Whatever food they had had to be consumed or preserved naturally. Because they did not have very good preservation methods, they were forced to eat only a meal or two a day for survival, which worked really well, unbeknownst to them. This is because their digestive systems were able to take a break from the grueling process of digestion giving the body an opportunity to redirect its energies to processes such as cell rejuvenation.

This continued for quite some time but as you know man, we are always looking for ways to innovate and make things easier, which is actually really good. But, is t good for our health?

So, what changed?

What caused the sudden shift from eating very healthy food and only eating it when you need it as opposed to eating food that is not good for our bodies and to make it worse, not being able to control ourselves in terms of only eating when we are hungry or when our bodies need to recharge and not eating after every hour?

Well, you may have guessed right, the agrarian revolution. As our ancestors tried to look for a way of feeding their families on a more regular basis and in a way that avoided the constant danger of encountering dangerous wild animals, they started to domesticate animals and plant their own food.

They had a really good gig going at this point but the fact that naturally, some humans are more ambitious than other, saw some of them expand their farming to even greater heights with their aim being to be able to supply other humans with food in exchange for something else.

People soon started realizing the need to add value to their food products in order to get more customers and beat the competition and this was the height of the agrarian revolution.

Processing became a major part of food production and with science and technology also peaking, people started realizing that there was a way of storing all these food without it getting spoiled.

Fast forward to date and the improvement in production is getting better and better especially with the sophistication of the science and technology in our current sphere.

Where exactly is the problem?

Scientifically and technological advancement is actually really good as this is something that enabled our ancestors to now be able to put a meal on the table without having to endanger their lives going into the forest looking for food. However, it is also important to look at the negative side of things. We have moved from eating food that naturally occurred as an animal or plant that wasn't even grown by man to food that we now process their seeds, as is the case for plants, and breed, as is the case for animals.

By default, there was a change in nutritional value in the sense that the former did not have any scientific influence by man and it grew naturally just as Mother Nature would have it. Today, our food is over processed. Even before food is planted, numerous experiments are conducted to ensure that that crop is able to grow without being affected by weeds or insects. Once the plant has grown and is harvested it is processed to get a number of different products, each being sold separately.

We have reached a point where you can buy grain produce that has been processed to the extent it has very little or even no fiber at all and very little nutritional value.

Animals too are heavily treated with antibiotics that our bodies read as toxins therein overworking our livers. It is no wonder that we are suffering from so many ailments. You now see why diverticulitis is a huge problem because we are now in an era where you have to do your due diligence to get a diet rich in all the essential nutrients. In the last decade we have seen the popularization of diets such as the paleo diet that are trying to take us back to living the lifestyle of our ancestors.

Eat for Health

Now that we have identified the problem, it is time for us to purposely eat for health and in a way that will help us prevent or reduce symptoms of diverticulitis. The first step is to eat food that is directly from a plant or animal.In this age of instant everything, it is very easy for you to fall for instant food that only need 5 to 1o minutes in your microwave or oven to be ready, especially after a long day at work. Take time during the weekend to go shopping in natural food stores, markets or pick-me-ups.

Secondly, natural food as we know it is highly perishable, so what could the food industry do to keep food on the shelves longer? Get rid of all aspects of food that make it go bad meaning strip it off all the nutrients and because without these the food would taste bland, replace the nutrients with artificial ingredients and taste enhancers that will never go bad and instead help whatever nutrients were left stay longer. We are talking about preservatives, additives, artificial sugars and fats.

What this means for you is that you are essentially eating 'dead food' since all living aspects of food have already been destroyed. If we borrow a saying from the world of computers, 'garbage in garbage out,' we are then dead men and women walking!

As we saw earlier, our bodies were designed to get their nutrients from real and natural food. What these over-processed foods do is to overwork our digestive systems as they try to extract nutrients that aren't there in the first place and also as they try to eliminate toxins in the name of additives and preservatives.

How Diverticulitis Develops

Inflammation, one of the greatest responses by your body as it tries to keep you safe, is one of the reasons why diverticulitis occurs.Ironical, right? Most of us are familiar with the fight or flight response from our bodies when faced with a situation that's deemed potentially dangerous by your body. This is a primal instinct that came in handy when our ancestors practiced hunting and gathering.It is meant to keep you safe and is usually triggered in specific situations that your brain deems to be harmful. However, today's lifestyle is such that we are continually exposed to stress. So you can imagine, your body responds to each stressful situation with the fight or flight response. Eventually your body gets worn out.

Some of the fight responses involve inflammation which can help a wound heal faster or protect you from allergenic or toxic substances or help a sprained joint heal faster by using pain to keep you from subjecting it to any weight.

When inflammation gets triggered on a near continuous basis, the communication between your brain and your adrenal glands gets scrambled. Your adrenals secret hormones that respond to particular situations. So, when this response is now continuous, the constant ineffective communication between your brain and adrenal glands tires your brain and this is the genesis of you experiencing unexplainable fatigue, lethargy and cognitive decline as your brain's effort of triggering response to increased stress is now changed into negative stress.

The fatigue you experience is from your body tirelessly trying to work to rid the stress it is registering to no avail and the fatigue is the first signal that something is not right. If this persists, your kidneys and liver are not able to function properly and toxins start accumulating in your body. Your liver gets so overwhelmed that it is not able to efficiently burn fat for energy, your digestive system is also not able to process the few nutrients you eat, if your diet is unhealthy, your blood vessels become thinner from clogging of fat and your heart is not able to pump blood effectively to all your organs and this is the onset of chronic illnesses.

With regard to diverticulitis, inflammation occurs as a result of constipation where you really strain to push out waste, causing slight injuries in your lower colon. Inflammation occurs so that these tears are healed faster and your lower colon can continue functioning well. However, when constipation now becomes chronic, the inner walls of your lower colon become very weak to the point where pouches are formed and these are the diverticular.

The problem with having diverticular is the fact that your digestive system is now left in a position where it is not able to stop food particles or fecal matter from being trapped inside the diverticular and with time, bacteria grow on these folds and spread. The fast thing a patient notices are pangs of sharp pain which are a sign that the patient has developed diverticulitis.

The Light at The End Of The Tunnel

The main aim of the eBook is to show you how to prevent diverticulitis and how to best manage symptoms if you have already been diagnosed with diverticulitis and we'll get right to it.

• Fiber, fiber, fiber!

Fiber is very important for digestion. However, when it comes to diverticulitis it fully depends on whether you are having a flare-up or not. When experiencing symptoms, it is advisable that you partake a low fiber diet that has low residue to avoid the chance of food getting trapped in the diverticular which could actually make things worse.

Once the flare-up is over and the symptoms have subsided, you can now introduce a natural high fiber diet. Y high fiber we mean about 30 grams of fiber in a day. The important thing is you slowly build up your fiber intake so you don't end up shocking your system that could in turn lead to gas formation, bloating and you getting the urge to push out gas, which could lead to diarrhea or pain.

The fiber we get from our food is either water soluble or water insoluble fiber. Soluble fiber includes pectin, mucilage and gum that is found in fruit or veggies whereas insoluble fiber includes peels and husks of fruit, veggies and grains. Legumes and oat bran are considered to contain soluble fiber.

- Drink up a lot of water

When you increase the amount of fiber in your diet, it is important that you also increase the amount of water you drink every day. Water also helps flush out waste thus ensuring you are straining to pass stool. Drink up at least 8 glasses of water every day for better health.

- Nuts and seeds

There is a very fine line between whether you should or shouldn't eat nuts and seeds if you have been diagnosed with diverticulitis. For so long, diverticulitis patients were advised by their doctors not to take nuts and seeds including fruit and veggies that have seeds such as strawberries, cucumbers and tomatoes with the argument being the small seeds could get lodged in the diverticular thus causing inflammation.

However, it has recently been revealed that when a patient is not experiencing a flare-up and is on a high fiber diet and drinking a lot of water, it is safe to eat nuts and seeds. Our advice is that you listen to your body and try nuts and seeds very little at a time. If the seeds trigger an attack it simply means you should not be eating them. On the other hand, if your body responds positively to them, then you can enjoy the new addition to your diet.

Diagnosis of Diverticulitis

So many patients who have diverticulitis do not show any symptoms. Most cases of diverticulitis are identified during a medical exam for another health condition. Gastroenterologists can easily identify and visualize the small diverticular pouches in the lower colon in procedures that involve a camera attached to a flexi tube with a light. It is also possible to identify diverticular during a colonoscopy or imaging procedures such as CT scans or x-rays.

Treatment

Diverticular do not disappear on their own. The good thing is that most patients do not experience symptoms. However, when diverticulitis is accompanied by constipation, bloating, severe abdominal pain, your doctor will recommend the amount of fiber you should be taking until the flare-up is over, after which your fiber intake will also change under advisement.

The recommended daily intake of fiber is 20 to 35 grams per day. However, so many of us don't even consume half of the recommended intake. A great part of prevention and 'treatment' of diverticulitis is increasing fiber intake from natural fruit, veggies and grains. Highly nutritious foods that have high fiber content include broccoli, apples, carrots, pears, squash and beans.

Your doctor may also recommend a fiber supplement such as polycarbophil, psyllium and methylcellulose which can either be in powder, pill or wafer form. This help soften and bulk up stool that make passing stool easier and also reduce spasms in your colon that happen especially when you don't have enough stool in the colon.

Can complications arise when you have diverticulitis?

If not addressed, diverticulitis can lead to infections, bleeding or colon blockage. When you present the symptoms of nausea, pain, constipation, chills, fever, or vomiting, your doctor may order for a series of tests. Infections that are not very serious are mostly treated with oral antibiotics. However, if infection continues without treatment, it leads to formation of abscess on the outer wall of the colon or inside the abdominal cavity (peritonitis). To diagnose an abscess, a CT scan has to be taken and once identified or confirmed the treatment involves intravenous antibiotic administration and drainage, when it's very severe.

A doctor may advise that a patient undergoes surgery to take out a portion of the infected colon when there are a series of repeated serious diverticulitis flare-ups.

Bleeding is another popular complication of diverticulitis that occurs when one of the pouches starts bleeding. This is the number cause of rectal bleeding for people above 40 years of age. It appears as dark red or maroon blood coming from the rectum. The good thing about this is that it typically stops on its own but when it takes too long to resolve itself, a colonoscopy is usually done to identify the problem.

In the case of intestinal blockage in the lower part of the colon, a surgery will have to be done to take out that part of the colon.

The most important thing is to watch your food and cut out as much processed food as you can and replace that with natural, whole foods and drink a lot of water.

How to Use this E-Book and Meal Plan

The inspiration for this book comes from the desire to spread a positive message on good health and to also shed more light on diverticulitis, how to prevent and manage it by leading a healthy lifestyle. We have created very tasty and healthy recipes, complete with a meal plan to make it very easy for you to prep all your meals.

The biggest takeaway from this eBook is that health is a lifestyle and not something that you do for a short period. Our aim is to go back to our ancestors' way of leaving that involved purely natural meals with the aim of helping our bodies heal themselves and function seamlessly.

The one thing you are going to really enjoy in this book is the recipe section. We have debunked the myth that healthy food is bland. Our recipes are super simple, super healthy and above all, mouthwateringly delicious.

The meal plan is to help you plan all the meals for the coming week by coming up with an ingredient list that you can shop for during the weekend. Our ingredients are very easy to find so you don't need to worry about visiting tens of shops to get a single ingredient.

The meal plan is also a simple guide of how to use the recipes. Once you are very familiar with all the recipes, feel free to create a meal plan that you feel captures your personality and schedule better. Also, feel free to tweak some of the recipes so you have your very own signature in the food you are cooking.

30-DAY HEALTHY COLON MEAL PLAN

Day	Breakfast	AM SNACK	Lunch	PM SNACK	Dinner
DAY 1	1 Serving Chilled Citrus Ginger Colon Shot	1 Glass Colon-Loving Green Juice	1 Serving Shiitake Mushrooms Soup + Mashed Potatoes	1 Glass Refreshing Citrus Cucumber Juice	1 Serving Delicious Low Carb Chicken Curry + A Bowl of White Rice
DAY 2	1 Serving Blueberry Superfood Green Smoothie	1 Glass Pineapple Aloe Vera Detox Juice	1 Serving Tamarind Sauce Fish Curry + White Rice	1 Glass Ultimate Stomach Elixir	1 Serving Broiled Steak with Shiitake Mushroom Sauce
DAY 3	1 Serving Minty Aloe Vera Orange Detox	1 Glass Refreshing Tomato Celery Juice	1 Serving Super Healing Broth + A Slice of White Bread	1 Glass Lemon Berry Juice	1 Serving Creamy Citrus Salmon Baked in Coconut Milk
DAY 4	1 Serving Turmeric Ginger Fenugreek Latte	1 Glass Ginger Pineapple Juice	1 Serving Warming Savory Soup + Cooked Pasta	1 Glass Spinach Ginger Juice	1 Serving Pan-Seared Lemon-Chili Salmon with Peppers & Potatoes
DAY 5	1 Serving Juice for Healthy Colon	1 GlassRefreshing Pineapple-Ginger Ale	1 Serving Creamy Detox Broccoli Soup + A slice of White Bread	1 Glass Super Stomach Cleanser Juice	1 Serving Spiced Roast Side of Salmon
DAY 6	1 Serving Low Carb Cinnamon Smoothie	1 Glass Healthy Green Detox Juice	1 Serving Citrus Chicken with Delicious Cold Soup + A Bowl White Rice	1 Glass Green Ginger Detoxifier	1 Serving Tilapia with Mushroom Sauce
DAY 7	1 Serving Stomach Upset Alleviator	1 Glass Vegetable Avocado Juice	1 Serving Stir-Fried Mushrooms & Golden Onions	1 Glass Hot Ginger Citrus Detox Drink	1 Serving Creamy Coconut Sardines Escabeche
DAY8	1 Serving Spiced Low Carb Coconut Milk Avocado Smoothie	1 GlassGarden Greens Juice	1 Serving Authentic and Easy Shrimp Curry with White Bread	1 Glass Green Asparagus Lemon Juice	1 Serving Lemon Mahi Mahi with Coconut Rice
DAY9	1 Serving Colon Cleanser	1 Glass Watermelon Green Detox Juice	1 Serving Healthy Spiced Carrot Soup + Mashed Potatoes	1 GlassNature's Super Blend Juice	1 Serving Citrus Grilled Beef with White Rice
DAY 10	1 Serving Almond Butter & Acai Smoothie	1 Glass Three-Ingredients Colon Detoxifier	1 Serving Shiitake Mushrooms & Chicken	1 Glass Hot Healthy Juice	1 Serving Hot Lemon Garlic Prawns with Rice

			Healing Soup + A slice of White Bread	
DAY 11	1 ServingUltimate Intestines Elixir	1 GlassStomach Healthy Detox Drink	1 Serving Colon Healing Broth + A bowl of White Rice	1 Glass Pineapple Aloe Vera Detox Juice	1 Serving Lemon & Garlic Grilled Trout
DAY 12	1 Serving Turmeric Smoothie	1 Glass Refreshing Citrus Cucumber Juice	1 Serving Healthy Veggie Soup + A bowl of Pasta	1 Glass Lemon Berry Juice	1 Serving Grilled Chicken Breast with Greek Yogurt
DAY 13	1 Serving Juice for Cleaner Stomach	1 Glass Detox Beet Juice	1 Serving Stomach Cleansing Broth + A Slice of White Bread	1 Glass Hot Ginger Citrus Detox Drink	1 Serving Fried Salmon Fillets with Mashed Potatoes
DAY 14	1 Serving Chocolate Peanut Butter Smoothie	1 GlassBerry Beet Juice	1 Serving Swahili Fish Curry with Rice	1 Glass Refreshing Pineapple-Ginger Ale	1 Serving Hot and Spiced Lemon Chicken Thighs
DAY 15	1 Serving Salmon with Avocado & Mushrooms Breakfast Bowl	1 Glass Green Ginger Detoxifier	1 Serving Ultimate Healthy Soup +A Slice of White Bread	1 Glass Watermelon Green Detox Juice	1 Serving Pan-Seared Lemon-Chili Salmon with Peppers & Potatoes
DAY 16	1 Serving Low Carb Coconut Flour Pancakes	1 Glass Super Body Detoxifier	1 Serving Hot Lemon Green Soup with Rice	1 Glass Green Asparagus Lemon Juice	1 Serving Delicious Low Carb Chicken Curry + A Bowl of White Rice
DAY 17	1 Serving Healthy Omelets with Greens & Shiitake Mushrooms	1 Glass Spinach Ginger Juice	1 Serving Coconut Milk Mushroom Soup + Mashed Potatoes	1 Glass Pineapple Aloe Vera Detox Juice	1 Serving Spiced Roast Side of Salmon
DAY 18	1 ServingAlmond Butter & Acai Smoothie	1 Glass Garden Greens Juice	1 Serving Yummy Squash Soup + A Bowl of Pasta	1 Glass Super Stomach Cleanser Juice	1 Serving Lobster with Herbed Lime-Jerk Butter
DAY 19	1 Serving Low Carb Smoked Salmon Omelet	1 Glass Nature's Super Blend Juice	1 Serving Lemon Leek & Broccoli Soup with White Rice	1 Glass Detox Beet Juice	1 Serving Grilled Chicken Breast with Greek Yogurt
DAY 20	1 Serving Low Carb Cinnamon Smoothie	1 Serving Refreshing Tomato Celery Juice	1 Serving Shiitake Mushrooms & Chicken Healing Soup + A slice of White Bread	1 Glass Berry Beet Juice	1 Serving Spiced Sichuan-Style Prawns + White Rice
DAY	1 Serving Spiced White Fish	1 Glass Stomach Healthy Detox	1 Serving Shiitake	1 Glass Hot Healthy Juice	1 Serving Lemon Mahi Mahi with

21	Breakfast Frittata	Drink	Mushrooms Soup + Mashed Potatoes		Coconut Rice
DAY 22	1 Serving Healthy Spiced Turmeric Cassava Pancakes	1 Glass Watermelon Green Detox Juice	1 Serving Stir-Fried Beef, Shiitake Mushrooms and Peppers	1 Glass Vegetable Avocado Juice	1 Serving Scrumptious Pot Roast Beef
DAY 23	1 Serving Spiced Egg Frittata	1 Glass Healthy Berry Juice	1 Serving Authentic and Easy Shrimp Curry with White Bread	1 Glass Green Asparagus Lemon Juice	1 Serving Broiled Steak with Shiitake Mushroom Sauce
DAY 24	1 Serving Chilled Citrus Ginger Colon Shot	1 Glass Green Ginger Detoxifier	1 Serving Tamarind Sauce Fish Curry + White Rice	1 Glass Healthy Green Detox Juice	1 Serving Red Snapper in Hot Veggie Sauce
DAY 25	1 ServingHealthy Lemony Blueberry Pancakes	1 Glass Garden Greens Juice	1 Serving Trinidadian Fish Stew With Mashed Potatoes	1 Glass Super Body Detoxifier	1 Serving Tilapia with Mushroom Sauce
DAY 26	1 Serving Blueberry Superfood Green Smoothie	1 Glass Hot Ginger Citrus Detox Drink	1 Serving Healthy Spiced Carrot Soup + Mashed Potatoes	1 Glass Ultimate Stomach Elixir	1 Serving Creamy Coconut Sardines Escabeche
DAY27	1 Serving Healthy Omelets with Greens & Shiitake Mushrooms	1 Glass Super Stomach Cleanser Juice	1 Serving Super Healing Broth + A Slice of White Bread	1 GlassRefreshing Pineapple-Ginger Ale	1 Serving Tasty Turkey Chili (Nut-Free, Gluten-Free) + Pasta
DAY 28	1 Serving Minty Aloe Vera Orange Detox	1 Glass Ginger Pineapple Juice	1 Serving Shiitake Mushrooms Soup + Mashed Potatoes	1 GlassSpinach Ginger Juice	1 Serving Delicious Low Carb Chicken Curry + A Bowl of White Rice
DAY 29	1 Serving Hot Scrumptious Egg Scramble	1 Glass Colon-Loving Green Juice	1 Serving Spiced Super Healthy Soup with White Rice	1 Glass Refreshing Tomato Celery Juice	1 Serving Creamy Citrus Salmon Baked in Coconut Milk
DAY 30	1 ServingTurmeric Ginger Fenugreek Latte	1 Glass Pineapple Aloe Vera Detox Juice	1 Serving Stir-Fried Beef, Shiitake Mushrooms and Peppers	1 Glass Refreshing Citrus Cucumber Juice	1 Serving Grilled Spiced Lemon Steak with Avocado Salad

BREAKFAST RECIPES

Blueberry Superfood Green Smoothie

Yield: 2 Servings

Total Time: 5 Minutes

Prep Time: 5 Minutes

Cook Time: N/A

Ingredients

- 1 cup frozen blueberries
- 1 cup frozen strawberries
- 2 cups diced red beets
- 1 cup kale, stems removed if desired
- 1 cup baby spinach
- 1 cup Greek yogurt, chilled
- 1 cup chilled fresh lemon juice
- 2 tablespoons minced ginger
- 1/2 cup frozen acai puree
- 2 tablespoons chia seeds
- 2 teaspoons spirulina powder

Directions

Blend everything together until very smooth. Serve right away.

Nutritional Information per Serving:

Calories: 160; Total Fat: 4 g; Carbs: 25.1 g; Dietary Fiber: 5 g; Sugars: 17.3 g Protein: 8.9 g; Cholesterol: 3 mg; Sodium: 89 mg

Turmeric Ginger Fenugreek Latte

Yield: 1 Serving

Total Time: 5 Minutes

Prep Time: 5 Minutes

Cook Time: 5 Minutes

Ingredients

- 1 cup skim milk
- 1 tablespoon fenugreek powder
- 1 teaspoon raw honey
- 1 teaspoon fresh lemon zest
- 1 teaspoon cinnamon
- 1 teaspoon ginger powder
- 1 teaspoon turmeric

Directions

Heat skim milk until hot; remove from heat and whisk un the remaining ingredients until very smooth and frothy. Enjoy!

Nutritional Information per Serving:

Calories: 197; Total Fat: 12 g; Carbs: 6 g; Dietary Fiber: 4 g; Sugar: 1 g; Protein: 0 g; Cholesterol: 13 mg; Sodium: 131 mg

Chilled Citrus Ginger Colon Shot

Yield: 1 Serving

Total Time: 15 Minutes

Prep Time: 15 Minutes

Ingredients

- 1 lemon
- 1 orange
- 1 lime
- 1 carrot
- 2 cm ginger
- 1 small stalk celery
- 1 clove garlic
- 1 sprig oregano
- 1 sprig parsley
- 1 teaspoon turmeric powder
- 1/2 cup water
- Ice

Directions

In a juicer, juice lemon, lime, ginger, garlic, orange, celery, parsley, carrots, and oregano. Add half a cup of water to wash out the remaining juice and stir the liquids together. Stir in turmeric, and camu camu until well combined. Serve over ice.

Nutritional Info Per Serving:

Calories: 101; Total Fat: 0 g; Carbs: 25 g; Dietary Fiber: 6 g; Sugars: 16 g; Protein: 2 g; Cholesterol: 0 mg; Sodium: 50 mg

Spiced Low Carb Coconut Milk Avocado Smoothie

Yield: 2 Servings

Prep Time: 5 Minutes

Ingredients

- 2 tablespoons fresh lemon juice
- 1/2 avocado
- 1/4 cup almond milk
- 3/4 cup full-fat coconut milk
- 1 teaspoon fresh grated ginger
- 1 scoop protein powder
- 1/2 teaspoon turmeric
- 1 cup crushed ice
- 1 teaspoon raw honey

Directions

Combine all ingredients in a blender and blend until very smooth. Enjoy!

Nutritional Information Per Serving

Calories: 208; Total Fat: 21 g; Carbs:5 g; Dietary fiber: 1.1; g; Sugars: 2.2 g; Protein: 11.9 g; Cholesterol: 9 mg; Sodium: 3 mg

Juice for Healthy Colon

Yield: 1 Serving

Total Time: 10 Minutes

Prep Time: 10 Minutes

Cook Time: N/A

Ingredients

- 2 potatoes
- 4 carrots
- 2-inch fresh ginger root
- 1 lemon
- 1 orange
- 1 tablespoon raw honey

Directions

In a blender, blend together all ingredients, except honey. Strain the liquid into a serving glass and stir in raw honey. Serve right away!

Low Carb Cinnamon Smoothie

Yield: 2 Servings

Prep Time: 5 Minutes

Ingredients

- 1/2 cup coconut milk
- 1 tablespoon ground chia seeds
- 1/2 teaspoon cinnamon
- 1 tablespoon MCT oil or coconut oil
- 1/2 cup water
- 1/4 cup vanilla whey protein

Directions

Combine all ingredients in a blender and blend until very smooth.

Sprinkle with more cinnamon to serve!

Nutritional Information Per Serving

Calories: 467; Total Fat: 40.3 g; Carbs: 4.7 g; Dietary fiber: 1.7; g; Sugars: 2.5 g; Protein: 23.6 g; Cholesterol: 4 mg; Sodium: 110 mg

Stomach Upset Alleviator

Yield: 1 Serving

Total Time: 10 Minutes

Prep Time: 10 Minutes

Cook Time: N/A

Ingredients

- 1 cup diced fresh pineapple
- 1 apple
- 1 grapefruit
- 1 lemon
- 4 carrots
- 4 cabbage leaves
- 2 garlic cloves
- 2-inch fresh ginger root

Directions

In a blender, blend together all ingredients. Strain the liquid into a serving glass and serve right away!

Colon Cleanser

Yield: 1 Serving

Total Time: 10 Minutes

Prep Time: 10 Minutes

Cook Time: N/A

Ingredients

- 2 lemons
- 4 cups raspberries
- 2-inch fresh ginger root
- 2-inch fresh turmeric root
- 1 tablespoon raw honey

Directions

In a blender, blend together all ingredients, except honey. Strain the liquid into a serving glass and stir in raw honey. Enjoy!

Juice for Cleaner Stomach

Yield: 1 Serving

Total Time: 10 Minutes

Prep Time: 10 Minutes

Cook Time: N/A

Ingredients

- 3 stalks of celery
- Half of an onion
- 1 clove of garlic
- 1 stalk of broccoli
- 1 grapefruit
- 1 orange
- 1 lemon
- 1 cup elderberries
- 1 teaspoon cinnamon
- 1 teaspoon cayenne pepper
- 1 tablespoon raw honey

Directions

In a blender, blend together all ingredients, except spices and honey. Strain the liquid into a serving glass and stir in cinnamon, cayenne pepper, and raw honey. Enjoy!

Minty Aloe Vera Orange Detox

Yield: 2 Servings

Prep Time: 10 Minutes

Ingredients:

- 3 organic oranges
- 2 fresh Aloe Vera branches
- 1 cup mint leaves
- 2-inch fresh ginger root

Directions

Slit the edges of aloe vera with a knife to open the outer layer; scoop out the gel and set aside. Wash and juice the oranges, mint leaves and ginger. Stir in aloe vera gel and serve right away.

Nutritional info per Serving:

Calories: 164; Total Fat: 0.8 g; Carbs: 39.6 g; Dietary Fiber: 9.9g; Sugars: 27.5 g; Protein: 4.2 g; Cholesterol: 0 mg; Sodium: 52 mg

Berry Aloe Detoxifier

Yield: 2 Servings

Prep Time: 10 Minutes

Ingredients

- 3 cucumbers
- 1 cup strawberries
- Handful fresh mint leaves
- 2-inch piece of fresh ginger
- 2 lemons
- 2 tablespoons aloe vera

Directions

Wash and juice veggies and fruits. Stir in aloe vera gel and serve.

Nutritional info per Serving:

Calories: 123; Total Fat: 1 g; Carbs: 30.8 g; Dietary Fiber: 5.6 g; Sugars: 14.2 g; Protein: 4.3 g; Cholesterol: 0 mg; Sodium: 50 mg

Almond Butter & Acai Smoothie

Yield: 1 Serving

Prep Time: 5 Minutes

Ingredients

- 1/4 of an avocado
- 3/4 cup unsweetened almond milk
- 1 tablespoon almond butter
- 2 tablespoons acai powder
- 1 tablespoon coconut oil
- 3 tablespoons protein powder
- 2 drops liquid stevia
- 1/2 teaspoon vanilla extract

Directions

Combine all ingredients in a blender and blend until very smooth. Enjoy!

Nutritional Information Per Serving

Calories: 345; Total Fat: 20.1 g; Carbs:8.1 g; Dietary fiber: 2.2; g; Sugars: 3.2 g; Protein: 15.3 g; Cholesterol: 4 mg; Sodium: 112 mg

Ultimate Intestines Elixir

Yield: 2 Servings

Prep Time: 10 Minutes

Ingredients

- 1 cup baby spinach
- A bunch of fresh wheatgrass
- 2-inch piece fresh ginger
- 1 apple
- 1 cucumber
- 2 celery stalks
- 2 teaspoons cayenne pepper
- 1 teaspoon turmeric

Directions

Wash and juice veggies and fruits. Stir in cayenne pepper and turmeric. Enjoy!

Nutritional info per Serving:

Calories: 208; Total Fat: 2 g; Carbs: 50.1 g; Dietary Fiber: 9.8 g; Sugars: 29.6 g; Protein: 4.7 g; Cholesterol: 0 mg; Sodium: 62 mg

Turmeric Smoothie

Yield: 1 Serving

Prep Time: 5 Minutes

Ingredients

- 1/2 cup unsweetened almond milk
- 1/2 cup full fat coconut milk
- 1 tablespoon coconut oil
- 1 teaspoon ground ginger
- 1 teaspoon ground cinnamon
- 1 tablespoon ground turmeric
- 1 scoop protein powder
- 1 teaspoon granulated sweetener
- 1 tablespoon Chia seeds

Directions

Combine all ingredients in a blender and blend until very smooth. Serve topped with chia seeds.

Nutritional Information Per Serving:

Calories: 250; Total Fat: 28.1 g; Carbs:4 g; Dietary fiber: 1.4; g; Sugars: 2.3 g; Protein: 17 g; Cholesterol: 4 mg; Sodium: 91 mg

Ginger Pineapple Wheatgrass Juice

Yield: 2 Servings

Prep Time: 10 Minutes

Ingredients

- 1 cup fresh diced pineapple
- A bunch of fresh wheatgrass leaves
- 2-inch knob of fresh ginger
- 2 cucumbers
- 2 celery stalks

Directions

Wash and juice veggies and fruits. Serve chilled!

Nutritional info per Serving:

Calories: 99; Total Fat: 0.5 g; Carbs: 23.9 g; Dietary Fiber: 3 g; Sugars: 13.5 g; Protein: 2.6 g; Cholesterol: 0 mg; Sodium: 22 mg

Chocolate Peanut Butter Smoothie

Yield: 1 Serving

Prep Time: 5 Minutes

Cook Time: N/A

Ingredients

- 1 tablespoon natural peanut butter
- 1 tablespoon unsweetened cocoa powder
- 1/2 cup almond milk
- Pinch of sea salt
- 1 teaspoon liquid stevia
- 1 scoop protein powder

Directions

Blend all ingredients together until smooth. Enjoy!

Nutritional Information per Serving:

Calories: 414; Total Fat: 34 g; Carbs: 13.3 g; Dietary Fiber: 2.4 g; Sugars: 4.6 g; Protein: 22.7 g; Cholesterol: 0 mg; Sodium: 219 mg

Salmon with Avocado & Mushrooms Breakfast Bowl

Yield: 2 Servings

Total Time: 25 Minutes

Prep Time: 10 Minutes

Cook Time: 15 Minutes

Ingredients

- 2 leftover grilled salmon fillets, chopped
- 1 tablespoon extra-virgin olive oil
- 1/2 pound mushrooms
- 2 cloves garlic
- 1 cup pureed tomatoes
- salt and pepper
- 1 tablespoon apple cider vinegar
- 1 tablespoon olive oil
- Avocado, diced

Directions

Heat olive oil in a pan over medium heat; sauté mushrooms, garlic and pureed tomatoes for about 5 minutes or until tender. Season with salt and pepper and transfer to a plate. Warm your leftover salmon and serve with the veggies drizzled with vinegar and avocado slices on the side.

Nutrition information per Serving:

Calories: 620; Total Fat: 45.3 g; Carbs: 19.3 g; Dietary Fiber: 10.1 g; Sugars: 5.9 g; Protein: 42.1 g; Cholesterol: 78 mg; Sodium: 122 mg

Healthy Spiced Turmeric Cassava Pancakes

Yield: 4 Servings

Total Time: 20 Minutes

Prep Time: 10 Minutes

Cook Time: 10 Minutes

Ingredients

- 3/4 cup cassava flour
- 1/2 cup coconut milk
- 2 free-range eggs
- 1/4 cup coconut oil, melted
- 1/2 teaspoon baking soda
- 1 teaspoon stevia
- 1 teaspoon ground ginger
- 1 teaspoon ground turmeric
- 1 teaspoon ground cinnamon
- 1/2 teaspoon ground black pepper

Directions

Mix together all dry ingredients in a large bowl.

In another bowl, whisk the eggs and then stir in coconut milk and coconut oil until well blended; add to the dry ingredients and whisk to form a smooth batter.

Heat a tablespoon of coconut oil in a medium skillet and cook in two spoonfuls of the batter for about 2 minutes; flip to cook the other side until golden brown. Repeat with the remaining batter. Serve topped with macadamia butter, coconut butter, and coconut flakes. Enjoy!

Nutritional Information per Serving:

Calories: 214 Total Fat: 28.1 g; Carbs: 20.5 g; Dietary Fiber: 1.5 g; Sugars: 1.1 g; Protein: 4.1 g; Cholesterol: 87 mg; Sodium: 228 mg

Hot Scrumptious Egg Scramble

Yield: 1 Serving

Total Time: 20 Minutes

Prep Time: 10 Minutes

Cook Time: 10 Minutes

Ingredients

- 1 teaspoon coconut oil
- 1/8 red onion, diced
- 1/8 Bell Pepper, diced
- 1 teaspoon hot sauce
- 2 free-range eggs
- 1/4 teaspoon red pepper flakes, crushed
- 1/4 teaspoon cumin
- Pinch of sea salt
- Pinch of pepper

Directions

Melt coconut oil in a nonstick skillet set over medium heat; stir in red onions and peppers and sauté for about 4 minutes or until onions are translucent.

Meanwhile, in a bowl, whisk together hot sauce, eggs, crushed red pepper flakes, cumin, salt and pepper until frothy; add to onion mixture and cook, stirring, until eggs are set. Season with salt and pepper and serve with mango chutney.

Nutrition Information per Serving:

Calories: 203; Total Fat: 15.9 g; Carbs: 4.7 g; Dietary Fiber: 1 g; Sugars: 2.7 g Protein: 11.8 g; Cholesterol: 327 mg; Sodium: 528 mg

Spiced Egg Frittata

Yield: 4 Servings

Total Time: 20 Minutes

Prep Time: 10 Minutes

Cook Time: 10 Minutes

Ingredients

- 5 eggs
- 1 teaspoon paprika
- 1 tablespoon curry powder
- ½ teaspoon salt
- ½ teaspoon pepper
- 1 tablespoon chopped cilantro
- 1 cup diced tomatoes
- 2 tablespoons coconut oil
- 1 Serrano pepper, minced
- 1 yellow onion, diced

Directions

Preheat your oven to 350 degrees.

Whisk together eggs, spices and cilantro in a bowl; set aside.

Heat oil in a skillet and then fry in serrano peppers, onions, and salt until onion is soft; add in tomatoes and cook, covered, for 10 minutes or until tomatoes are soft. Add in the egg mixture and stir in to combine. Cook for about 5 minutes and then transfer to the oven. Bake for about minutes or until the egg is set. Serve hot with chai masala.

Nutritional Info per Serving:

Calories: 164; Total Fat: 1.9 g; Carbs: 6.3 g; Dietary Fiber: 2 g; Sugars: 3 g; Protein: 7.9 g; Cholesterol: 205 mg; Sodium: 373 mg

Coconut Milk Mushroom Soup

Yield: 4 Servings

Total Time: 15 Minutes

Prep Time: 10 Minutes

Cook Time: 5 Minutes

Ingredients

1 ½ pounds mushroom, trimmed

1 clove garlic, minced

2 red onions, chopped

4 cups vegetable stock

2 cups coconut milk

1/8 teaspoon sea salt

1/8 teaspoon pepper

Directions

Grill the mushrooms, turning frequently, for about 5 minutes or until charred and tender; set aside. In a soup pot, sauté red onion in a splash of water. Stir in vegetable stock and cook for a few minutes. Place the onions and mushrooms in a blender; blend until very smooth; add coconut milk, garlic, and thyme and continue blending until very smooth and creamy.

Return the soup to the pot and season with salt, and pepper.

Enjoy!

Nutritional Information per Serving:

Calories: 338; Total Fat: 29.2 g; Carbs: 18.1 g; Dietary Fiber: 5.8 g; Sugars: 9.3 g; Protein: 8.8 g; Cholesterol: 0 mg; Sodium: 89 mg

Hot Lemon Green Soup with Rice

Yield: 4-6 Servings
Total Time: 1 Hour 15 Minutes
Prep Time: 15 Minutes
Cook Time: 60 Minutes

Ingredients

- 1 pound curly kale, torn
- 12 ounces baby spinach
- ¼ cup white rice, rinsed
- 2 yellow onions, chopped
- 2 tablespoons olive oil
- 3 cups plus 2 tablespoons water
- 4 cups homemade vegetable broth
- 1 tablespoon fresh lemon juice
- 1 large pinch of cayenne pepper
- Salt, to taste

Directions

Add the two tablespoons of olive oil in a large pan and cook the onions over medium heat. Sprinkle with salt and cook for 5 minutes until they start browning. Lower the heat and pour in two tablespoons of water. Cover and lover the heat and cook for 25 minutes until the onions caramelize, stirring frequently.

Meanwhile, add the remaining water and some salt to a Dutch oven and stir in the rice. Bring to a boil then lower the heat and simmer for about 15 minutes until tender. Stir in the kale into the cooked rice, cover and cook for 10 more minutes.

Add the onions to the rice mixture together with the broth, spinach and cayenne and simmer for 5 minutes. Use an immersion blender to puree the rice mixture until smooth then stir in the lemon juice. Serve into soup bowls and drizzle each with some olive oil.

Nutritional Information per Serving:

Calories: 102; Total Fat: 7.4 g; Carbs: 8.3g; Dietary Fiber: 3.1g; Sugars: 2.8 g; Protein: 3.1 g; Cholesterol: 0 mg; Sodium: 109 mg

Ultimate Healthy Soup

Yield: 6 Servings

Total Time: 35 Minutes

Prep Time: 15 Minutes

Cook Time: 20 Minutes

Ingredients

- 2 tablespoons extra-virgin olive oil
- 1 cup chopped shallot
- 1 tablespoon grated ginger
- 2 cloves garlic, minced
- 4 cups homemade chicken broth
- 1 medium golden beet, diced
- 1 large carrot, sliced
- 1 cup shredded red cabbage
- 1 cup sliced mushrooms
- a handful of pea pods, halved
- 1 hot chili pepper, sliced
- 1 cup chopped cauliflower
- 1 cup chopped broccoli
- 1 bell pepper, diced
- A pinch of cayenne pepper
- A pinch of sea salt
- 1 cup baby spinach
- 1 cup chopped kale

- 1 cup grape tomatoes, halved

Directions

In a large skillet, heat olive oil until hot but not smoky; sauté in shallots, ginger and garlic for about 2 minutes or until tender; stir in broth and bring the mixture to a gentle simmer. Add in beets and carrots and simmer for about 5 minutes.

Stir in hot pepper, cauliflower and broccoli and cook for about 3 minutes. stir in bell pepper, red cabbage, mushrooms, and peas and cook for 1 minute. Remove from heat and stir in salt and pepper. Stir in leafy greens and tomatoes and cover the pot for about 5 minutes. Serve.

Citrus Chicken with Delicious Cold Soup

Yield: 4 Servings

Total Time: 45 Minutes

Prep Time: 15 Minutes

Cook Time: 30 Minutes

Ingredients

- 2 tablespoons extra-virgin olive oil
- 500g ounces chicken breast
- 1 teaspoon fresh rosemary
- 1 lemon, sliced
- 1 orange, sliced

For the Cold Soup

- 2 tablespoons apple cider vinegar
- 1/4 cup green pepper, chopped
- 1/4 cup cucumber, chopped
- 1/2 cup onion, chopped
- 3 cloves garlic, minced
- 1 cup stewed tomatoes

Directions

Generously coat chicken with extra virgin olive oil and cover with rosemary, lemon and orange slices. Bake in the oven at 350°F for about 30 minutes.

In a blender, blend together all the soup ingredients until very smooth and then serve with chicken and cooked brown rice.

Nutritional Information per Serving:

Calories: 438; Total Fat: 9 g; Carbs: 19.9 g; Dietary Fiber: 4.5 g; Sugars: 12.8 g; Protein: 46.2 g; Cholesterol: 131 mg; Sodium: 139 mg

Stomach Cleansing Broth

Yield: 6 Servings
Total Time: 30 Minutes
Prep Time: 10 Minutes
Cook Time: 20 Minutes

Ingredients

- 1/4 cup water
- 2 cloves garlic, minced
- 1/2 cup chopped red onion
- 1 tablespoon minced fresh ginger
- 1 cup chopped tomatoes
- 1 small head of broccoli, chopped into florets
- 3 medium carrots, diced
- 3 celery stalks, diced
- 1/8 teaspoon cayenne pepper
- 1/4 teaspoon cinnamon
- 1 teaspoon turmeric
- Sea salt and pepper
- 6 cups vegetable broth
- ¼ cup fresh lemon juice
- 1 cup chopped purple cabbage
- 2 cups chopped kale

Directions

Boil ¼ cup of water in a large pot; add garlic and onion and sauté for about 2 minutes, stirring. Stir in ginger, tomatoes, broccoli, carrots and celery and cook for about 3 minutes. Stir in spices

Add in vegetable broth and bring the mixture to a boil; lower heat and simmer for about 15 minutes or until veggies are tender. Stir in lemon juice, cabbage and kale and cook for about 2 minutes or until kale is wilted. Adjust the seasoning and serve hot.

Nutritional Information per Serving:

Calories: 84; Total Fat: 1.7 g; Carbs: 10.8 g; Dietary Fiber: 2.1 g; Sugars: 4.1 g; Protein: 6.6 g; Cholesterol: 0 mg; Sodium: 808 mg

Trinidadian Fish Stew With Mashed Potatoes

Yield: 2 Servings

Total Time: 40 Minutes

Prep Time: 15 Minutes

Cook Time: 25 Minutes

Ingredients

- 200g white fish fillets
- 2 tablespoons lime zest
- 1/2 cup lime juice
- 1/2 cup fresh lemon juice
- ½ teaspoon white pepper
- 2 tablespoons chopped thyme
- 1 tablespoon dark rum
- 3 tablespoons vegetable oil
- 1 red onion, chopped
- 2 cloves garlic, chopped
- 1 tablespoon chopped coriander
- 3 tomatoes, chopped
- 2 teaspoons dark muscovado sugar
- Mashed potatoes to serve

Directions

In a dish, combine lime juice and zest; place the fish in the dish and pour the lemon juice over the fish.In a mortar, crush together thyme leaves, white pepper and salt into a paste; pour over the fish and gently massage the mixture into the fish. Pour in rum and cover the dish; let marinate in the refrigerator for about 1 hour. Heat oil in a pan and cook in onion for about 5 minutes or until tender; stir in garlic, coriander, tomatoes and sugar for about 4 minutes or until tomatoes are tender. Remove the fish from the marinade and place in the pan; pour in the marinade and cover the pan.

Cook for about 8 minutes or until the fish is cooked through. Season with sea salt and pepper and serve with mashed potatoes.

Nutrition Information per Serving:

Calories: 388; Total Fat: 19 g; Carbs: 17 g; Dietary Fiber: 2 g; Sugar: 5 g; Protein: 35 g; Sodium: 310 mg; Cholesterol: 0 mg

Swahili Fish Curry with Rice

Yield: 4 Servings
Total Time: 30 Minutes
Prep Time: 10 Minutes
Cook Time: 20 Minutes

Ingredients

- 4 skinless white fish fillets
- 2 tablespoons fresh juice
- 2 tablespoons Caribbean curry powder
- 1 tablespoon groundnut oil
- 1 cup sliced spring onions
- 2-inch ginger root, grated
- 2 cloves garlic, crushed
- 1 scotch bonnet chilli, chopped
- 1 red pepper, chopped
- 1 teaspoon chopped thyme
- 2 cups coconut milk
- 4 cups cooked rice

Directions

Mix lemon juice and half of the Caribbean curry powder and rub onto the fish; let sit for a few minutes.

Heat oil in a pan and cook in onion, garlic, chilli, ginger, and pepper for about 5 minutes. stir in thyme and the remaining curry powder for about 1 minute. Add in coconut milk and simmer for about 10 minutes or until the sauce is thick. Add in the fish and simmer, covered, for about 10 minutes or until the fish is cooked through. Serve over cooked rice topped with fresh thyme.

Nutrition Information per Serving:

Calories: 314; Total Fat: 21 g; Carbs: 7 g; Dietary Fiber: 3 g; Sugar: 4 g; Protein: 29 g; Sodium: 400 mg; Cholesterol: 0 mg

DINNER

Lobster with Herbed Lime-Jerk Butter

Yield: 4 Servings

Total Time: 35 Minutes

Prep Time: 15 Minutes

Cook Time: 20 Minutes

Ingredients

- 1 tablespoons melted butter
- 2-pound lobster, cleaned, halved
- 1/2 cup chopped onion
- 1/2 cup sweet pepper, chopped
- 1 tablespoon Jamaican jerk seasoning
- 1/4 cup rum
- 3 tablespoons butter
- 1/4 cup fresh lime juice
- 1/4 cup chopped chives and parsley

Directions

Boil lobster in water until bright red; transfer to a baking dish; drizzle with a tablespoon of butter and bake in a 300-degrees oven for about 15 minutes.

Meanwhile, melt the remaining butter and sauté onion, sweet pepper, and jerk seasoning. Remove from heat and stir in rum until well blended. Stir in herbs and lime juice. Serve the baked lobster drizzled with the lime butter.

Nutrition Information per Serving:

Calories: 362; Total Fat: 14 g; Carbs: 6 g; Dietary Fiber: 2 g; Sugar: 3 g; Protein: 44 g; Sodium: 1107 mg; Cholesterol: 362 mg

Grilled Spiced Lemon Steak with Avocado Salad

Yield: 4 Servings
Total Time: 20 Minutes
Prep Time: 10 Minutes
Cook Time: 10 Minutes

Ingredients

- 1 pound flank steak
- 4 tablespoons fresh lemon juice
- 2 tablespoons extra-virgin olive oil
- 1 teaspoon turmeric powder
- 1 tablespoon minced garlic
- 1 tablespoon minced ginger
- 1 teaspoon cayenne pepper
- ½ teaspoon sea salt
- 1 avocado, sliced
- 4 cups sliced tomatoes
- ½ cup fresh lemon juice

Directions

Whisk together fresh lemon juice, olive oil, turmeric powder, minced garlic, minced ginger, sea salt, and cayenne pepper; brush over the steak and grill on a preheated grill for about 5 minutes per side or until cooked to your likeness. Transfer the meat to a cutting board and let rest for at least 5 minutes.

Divide avocado slices and tomatoes among serving plates and top each with sliced grilled steak. Drizzle with fresh lemon juice and sprinkle with a pinch of salt and black pepper. Enjoy!

Nutritional Information per Servings:

Calories: 216; Total Fat: 11 g; Carbs: 4 g; Dietary Fiber: 1.3 g; Sugars: 1 g; Protein: 26 g; Cholesterol: 70 mg; Sodium: 390 mg

Roasted Sea Bass with Oregano

Yield: 4 Servings
Total Time: 35 Minutes
Prep Time: 15 Minutes
Cook Time: 20 Minutes

Ingredients

- 2 medium-sized whole sea bass
- 1 tablespoon extra-virgin olive oil
- 2 garlic cloves, thinly sliced
- ½ teaspoon dried oregano
- 2 teaspoons freshly squeezed lemon juice
- 2 tablespoons fresh pineapple juice
- Kosher salt and freshly ground pepper, to taste
- 2 lemons, thinly sliced

Directions

Start by preheating your broiler or grill to medium-high heat. Lightly grease the rack with olive oil cooking spray.

Combine the lemon juice, olive oil, salt, pepper and oregano in a bowl and let stand. Use a sharp knife to make 3 horizontal slits on each side of the fish and rub with some kosher salt. Use a brush to rub in the lemon-herb mixture in the slits.

Cook the fish in the reheated broiler/ grill for about 15-20 minutes, turning twice in between cook time and baste with the lemon-oregano mixture. Grill until the flesh turns opaque or until desired doneness is achieved. Let the sea bass rest for 50-10 minutes before serving. Serve with steamed veggies or a salad.

Enjoy!

Nutritional Information per Serving:

Calories: 236; Total Fat: 16 g; Carbs: 3 g; Dietary Fiber 1g; Sugars: 1 g; Protein: 37 g; Cholesterol: 0 mg; Sodium: 563 mg

Delicious Low Carb Chicken Curry

Yield: 1 Serving

Total Time: 30 Minutes

Prep Time: 10 Minutes

Cook Time: 20 Minutes

Ingredients

- 100 grams chicken, diced
- ¼ cup chicken broth
- Pinch of turmeric
- Dash of onion powder
- 1 tablespoon minced red onion
- Pinch of garlic powder
- ¼ teaspoon curry powder
- Pinch of sea salt
- Pinch of pepper
- Stevia, optional
- Pinch of cayenne

Directions

In a small saucepan, stir spices in chicken broth until dissolved; stir in chicken, garlic, onion, and stevia and cook until chicken is cooked through and liquid is reduced by half. Serve hot.

Nutritional Information per Serving:

Calories: 170; Total Fat: 3.5 g; Carbs: 2.3 g; Dietary Fiber: 0.6 g; Sugars: 0.8 g; Protein: 30.5 g; Cholesterol: 77 mg; Sodium: 255 mg

Creamy Citrus Salmon Baked in Coconut Milk

Yields: 4 Servings
Total Time: 35 Minutes
Prep Time: 15 Minutes
Cook Time: 25 Minutes

Ingredients

- 1 teaspoon coconut oil
- 4 salmon fillets
- 3 tablespoons freshly squeezed lemon juice
- 3 tablespoons freshly squeezed lime juice
- 3 tablespoons freshly squeezed orange juice
- 1 cup coconut milk
- 1 teaspoon ground pepper
- 1 teaspoon sea salt
- 1 teaspoon dried parsley flakes
- 1 finely chopped clove garlic

Directions

Preheat your oven to 190°C (275°F). Coat a baking dish with coconut oil. Rinse the fish under water and pat dry with paper towels.

Melt coconut oil in a skillet set over medium heat and add in salmon fish; cook for about 5 minutes per side of until browned on both sides.

Transfer the fish fillet to the coated baking dish and drizzle with coconut milk, lemon, lime, and orange juices. Sprinkle with ground pepper, sea salt, parsley, and garlic.

Bake in the oven for about 15 minutes or until the flakes easily when touched with a fork. Serve with a bowl of cooked brown rice or quinoa.

Nutritional Information per Serving:

Calories: 248; Total Fat: 12g; Carbs: 0.7g; Dietary Fiber: trace; Protein: 34.8g; Cholesterol: 0mg; Sodium: 82mg; trace

Tilapia with Mushroom Sauce

Yields: 4 Servings
Total Time:35 Minutes
Prep Time: 15 Minutes
Cook Time: 20 Minutes

Ingredients

- 6 ounces tilapia fillets
- 2 teaspoon arrow root
- 1 cup mushrooms, sliced
- 1 clove garlic, finely chopped
- 1 small onion, thinly sliced
- 2 tablespoons extra-virgin olive oil
- ½ cup fresh parsley, roughly chopped
- 1 teaspoon thyme leaves, finely chopped
- ½ cup water
- A pinch of freshly ground black pepper
- A pinch of sea salt

Directions

Preheat your oven to 350°F. Add extra virgin olive oil to a frying pan set over medium heat; sauté onion, garlic and mushrooms for about 4 minutes or until mushrooms are slightly tender.

Stir in arrowroot, sea salt, thyme and pepper and cook for about 1 minute.

Stir in water until thickened; stir in parsley and cook for 1 minute more. Place the fillets on a baking tray lined with parchment paper; cover the fish with mushroom sauce and bake for about 20 minutes or until the fish is cooked through.

Nutritional Information per Serving:

Calories: 177; Total Fat: 7.2 g; Carbs: 3.3 g; Dietary Fiber: 1.4 g; Sugars: 1.1 g; Protein: 14.9 g; Cholesterol: 1 mg; Sodium: 66 mg

Jerk Spiced Chicken Wings

Yields: 3 Servings

Total Time: 20 Minutes

Prep Time: 5 Minutes

Cook Time: 15 Minutes

Ingredients

- 18 chicken wings
- Jerk seasoning blend
- I can pineapples (crushed)
- 2 tablespoons mustard sauce
- 2 tablespoons
- Low sodium soy sauce
- 2 cups BBQ sauce
- 1/3 cup dark brown sugar
- 1 teaspoon freshly ground black pepper
- Sea salt to taste

Directions

Set your grill on medium-high heat.

Generously rub the chicken wings with jerk seasoning, salt and pepper. Mix the remaining ingredients to make the barbeque sauce. Grill the wings for about 10-15 minutes, turning halfway through until cooked. Brush with the barbeque sauce and continue grilling on low for 2-5 minutes as you keep basting.

Serve hot with mashed or roast potatoes.

Nutrition Information per Serving:

Calories: 327; Total Fat: 15.8 g; Carbs: 17.1 g; Dietary Fiber:1.1 g; Sugar: 8 g; Protein: 21.1 g; Sodium: 1287 mg; Cholesterol: 63 mg

Spiced Roast Side of Salmon

Yield: 6 Servings

Total Time: 30 Minutes

Prep Time: 10 Minutes

Cook Time: 20 Minutes

Ingredients

- 1 tablespoon olive oil
- 1½ kg side of salmon
- 1 teaspoon honey
- 1 tablespoon wholegrain mustard
- ½ teaspoon black peppercorns
- 1 teaspoon paprika
- ½ teaspoon ground ginger
- 1 lemon, cut into wedges

Directions

Preheat your oven to 350 degrees and prepare a roasting tin by lining it with foil. Brush the fish with oil and place in the tin, skin side down.

In a small bowl, mix together a teaspoon of olive oil, honey, mustard, pepper and paprika and then smear the mixture onto the salmon.

Roast the fish in the oven for 20 minutes or until cooked through. Serve with lemon wedges. Enjoy!

Nutritional Information per Serving:

Calories: 482; Total Fat: 30 g; Carbs: 2 g; Dietary Fiber: 0 g; Sugars: 1 g; Protein: 51 g; Cholesterol: 0 mg; Sodium: 400 mg

Pan-Seared Lemon-Chili Salmon with Peppers & Potatoes

Yield: 4 Servings

Total Time: 25 Minutes

Prep Time: 10 Minutes

Cook Time: 10 Minutes

Ingredients

- 1 ¼ pounds salmon fillet, sliced into 4 parts
- 2 medium bell peppers, sliced
- 1 pound diced potatoes
- 2 tablespoons extra-virgin olive oil
- ½ teaspoon garlic powder
- 1 teaspoon ground cumin
- 2 teaspoons chili powder
- ¼ teaspoon ground pepper
- ¾ teaspoon sea salt
- 2 tablespoons fresh lemon zest
- Lemon wedges to serve

Directions

Preheat your oven to 425 degrees. Grease a rimmed baking sheet with olive oil and set aside.

In a bowl, toss together a tablespoon of olive oil, potatoes, tomatoes, sea salt and pepper and transfer to the prepared baking sheet. Roast for about 15 minutes.

In the meantime, mix together garlic powder, cumin, chili powder, salt and lemon zest.

Add the bell peppers to a large bowl and add in the remaining oil and half of the lemon zest spice mixture.

Coat the fish with the remaining spice mix.

Remove the baking sheet from the oven and stir in the peppers; roast for an additional 5 minutes and add in the salmon. Roast for 6 minutes or until the fish is cooked through.

Serve the fish with the roasted potatoes garnished with lemon wedges.

Nutritional Information per Servings:

Calories: 405; Total Fat: 17.4 g; Carbs: 25.9 g; Dietary Fiber: 3 g; Sugars: 3 g; Protein: 35.4 g; Cholesterol: 90 mg; Sodium: 517 mg

Broiled Steak with Shiitake Mushroom Sauce

Yield: 4 Servings

Total Time: 35 Minutes

Prep Time: 10 Minutes

Cook Time: 25 Minutes

Ingredients

- 1 pound lean flank steak
- ½ teaspoon sea salt
- ½ teaspoon black pepper
- 1 teaspoon extra-virgin olive oil

Shiitake Mushroom Sauce:

- 2 cups sliced shiitake mushrooms
- 1 cup chopped red onions
- 4 garlic cloves, minced
- 1 cup homemade beef broth
- 1/4 cup fresh lemon juice
- 1 cup minced green onions

Directions

Preheat your broiler.

Sprinkle the steak with salt and pepper and place in a broiler pan; drizzle with olive oil and broil for about 5 minutes or until cooked to your likeness. Remove the meat from the oven and keep warm in a foil. Heat a skillet over medium high heat and add in olive oil; sauté red onion and garlic for about 2 minutes. stir in shiitake mushrooms for about 5 minutes and then stir in broth; bring to a boil. Lower heat and simmer for about 6 minutes and then stir in green onions. Stir in lemon juice and cook for 2 minutes.

Slice the steak and serve with the mushroom sauce.

Nutritional Information per Servings:

Calories: 203; Total Fat: 8 g; Carbs: 6.1 g; Dietary Fiber: 1.2 g; Sugars: 2.4 g; Protein: 25.3 g; Cholesterol: 43 mg; Sodium: 462 mg

Creamy Coconut Sardines Escabeche

Yield: 6 Servings

Total Time: 48 Minutes

Prep Time: 20 Minutes

Cook Time: 38 Minutes

Ingredients

- 1kg fresh sardines
- 150ml extra virgin olive oil
- 1 red onion, thinly sliced
- 1 carrot, thinly sliced
- 2 garlic cloves, thinly sliced
- 4 tablespoons sherry vinegar
- 2 cups coconut milk
- ½ cup coconut cream
- 2 tablespoons chopped flat-leaf parsley
- 2 fresh bay leaves
- 1 teaspoon black peppercorns
- 3-4 thyme sprigs
- 1 teaspoon cumin seeds
- 3 tablespoons almond flour

Directions

Wash the sardines with warm water and dry with paper towel; mix flour with salt and pepper and then dust the sardines with the flour.

Heat half of the oil in a pan set over medium heat and cook the sardines in batches for about 5 minutes per side or until cooked through and lightly browned; transfer to a dish and clean the pan, add in the remaining oil and sauté the onions for about 4 minutes or until lightly browned; stir in garlic and carrots and cook for another minute. Stir in the coconut milk along with remaining ingredients and simmer for about 5 minutes or until liquid is by half; add in sardines and stir to coat well. Cook for about 2 minutes and then remove from heat. Serve with brown rice.

Nutrition information per Serving:

Calories: 568; Total Fat: 41 g; Carbs: 7 g; Dietary Fiber: 2 g; Sugars: 2 g; Protein: 41 g; Cholesterol: 108 mg; Sodium: 84 mg;

Scrumptious Pot Roast Beef

Yield 4 Servings

Total Time: 3Hours 45 Minutes

Prep Time: 10 Minutes

Cook Time: 3 Hours 35 Minutes

Ingredients

- 3 pounds chuck roast (boneless)
- 1 scotch bonnet chili, seeded and sliced
- 10 allspice (pimento) seeds, crushed
- 1 yellow onion
- ¼ cup soy sauce (mushroom)
- 4 garlic cloves, minced
- 1/3 cup thinly sliced green onion
- 1 cup water
- 2 tablespoons canola oil

Directions

Mix the soy sauce, scotch bonnet, crushed pimento seeds, garlic and yellow onion in a small bowl.

Make one inch incisions on the chuck roast and fill them with the spice blend. Set aside the remaining mixture.Brown the chuck roast in oil for about 5 minutes over medium-high heat until evenly browned. Add the remaining spice mix and 1 cup of water and simmer over medium heat for 30 minutes. Preheat your oven at 225 degrees F.

Transfer in the oven and cook for 3 hours or until tender. Top with spring onions. Serve with steamed veggies or green salad.

Nutrition Information per Serving:

Calories: 468; Total Fat: 16.9 g; Carbs: 21 g; Dietary Fiber:1.6 g; Sugar: 11.8 g; Protein: 26 g; Sodium: 1922 mg; Cholesterol: 176 mg

Curried Prawns with White Bread

Yield 4 Servings
Total Time: 1 Hour
Prep Time: 15 Minutes
Cook Time: 25 Minutes

Ingredients

- 225g jumbo prawns, peeled
- 1 cup vegetable stock
- 1 inch ginger root, thinly stripped
- 1 red chili, seeded and thinly sliced
- 1 can coconut milk
- 2 tablespoons hot curry powder
- 75 g sugar snap peas
- 1 large sweet potato, cubed
- Juice of 1 lime
- ½ cup thinly sliced spring onions for serving
- Salt and pepper to taste

Directions

Toast the coconut in a large pan for about 2 minutes until it turn golden. Transfer into a bowl. Return the pan to heat and add curry powder and toast it until fragrant for about a minute then add in the sweet potato cubes, chili and ginger. Pour in the stock and coconut milk and bring to a boil. Lower the heat and simmer for 10 minutes until the potatoes are tender. Stir in the veggies and cook for 5 minutes until soft. Next add the prawns and cook for about 2 minutes or until they turn pink. Season the curry. Turn of the heat and stir in the spring onions and lime juice.
Serve with artisan bread and top with toasted coconut

Nutrition Information per Serving:

Calories: 367,; Total Fat: 16.5 g; Carbs: 33.5 g; Dietary Fiber:1.9 g; Sugar: 13 g; Protein: 26 g; Sodium: 1198 mg; Cholesterol: 112 mg

Hot Lemon Garlic Prawns with Rice

Yield: 8 Servings

Total Time: 35 Minutes

Prep Time: 15 Minutes

Cook Time: 20 Minutes

Ingredients

- 1kg raw prawns, peeled, deveined
- 2 cups white rice
- 4 cups water
- ½ teaspoon sea salt
- 2 tablespoons olive oil
- 2 tablespoons coconut oil
- 1 shallot, chopped
- 4 garlic cloves, chopped
- 2 tablespoons minced ginger
- 1/2 teaspoon chilli flakes
- 1/2 teaspoon fennel seeds
- 1 teaspoon ground paprika
- 1/2 cup fresh lemon juice
- 2 tablespoons fresh lemon zest
- 2 tablespoon chopped parsley

Directions

In a large pot, combine olive oil, sea salt and water; stir in white rice and simmer, covered, for about 20 minutes or until rice is cooked through. Remove from heat and fluff with a spoon to cool.

Heat coconut oil in a skillet over medium heat and stir in shallots, fennel seeds, and chilli flakes for about 2 minutes or until shallots are tender. Stir in garlic, ginger, paprika and prawns, sea salt and pepper and cook for about 5 minutes or until the prawns are cooked through. Remove the pan from heat and stir in fresh lemon juice, lemon zest and parsley.

Serve the prawn and sauce over a bowl of cooked white rice.

Nutritional Information per Servings:

Calories: 311; Total Fat: 12 g; Carbs: 11 g; Dietary Fiber: 2.7 g; Sugars: 3 g; Protein: 15 g; Cholesterol: 189 mg; Sodium: 557 mg

Lemon Mahi Mahi with Coconut Rice

Yield: 4 Servings

Total Time: 40 Minutes

Prep Time: 10 Minutes

Cook Time: 30 Minutes

Ingredients

4 (150-gram) skinless Mahi Mahi fillets

½ teaspoon paprika

1/2 cup fresh lemon juice

½ teaspoon sea salt

½ teaspoon black pepper

4 tablespoons coconut oil

4 cups white rice

1 cup coconut milk

Lemon wedges

Directions

Preheat your oven to 385 degrees. Season the Mahi Mahi fish with fresh lemon juice, paprika, sea salt, and black pepper.

Heat a tablespoon of oil in a skillet and sear the seasoned fish for about 3 minutes per side or until golden browned.

Transfer to a baking pan and bake for about 10 minutes or until the fish is cooked through.

Combine coconut milk, salt and olive oil in a pan; stir in rice and cook for about 20 minutes or until rice is cooked through.

Serve the fish with the coconut rice.

Citrus Grilled Beef with White Rice

Yield: 3 Servings

Total Time: 15 Minutes

Prep Time: 10 Minutes

Cook Time: 5 Minutes

Ingredients

- 350g lean beef steak
- 2 tablespoons freshly squeezed orange juice
- 2 tablespoons freshly squeezed lemon juice
- 2 tablespoons freshly squeezed lime juice
- 3 tablespoons extra-virgin olive oil
- 1 teaspoon raw honey
- 1 teaspoon raw apple-cider vinegar
- ¼ teaspoon coarse salt
- ¼ teaspoon black pepper
- 3 cups cooked white rice

Directions

In a bowl, whisk together the dressing juices, olive oil, honey, apple cider vinegar, salt and pepper until well combined; add in the meat and let marinate for at least 30 minutes.

Preheat your grill on medium heat; grill the steak for about 8 minutes per side or until golden browned on the outside and cooked through. Let cool and slice into small pieces. Serve with cooked white rice and a glass of juice.

Nutritional Information per Serving:

Calories: 315; Fat: 25.8 g; Carbs: 4.8 g; Dietary Fiber: 1.2 g; Sugars: 1.2 g; Protein: 39.3 g; Cholesterol: 255 mg; Sodium: 581 mg

Lemon & Garlic Grilled Trout

Yield: 8 Servings

Total Time: 40 Minutes

Prep Time: 25 Minutes

Cook Time: 15 Minutes

Ingredients

- 1.5kg piece trout fillet
- 2 tablespoons lemon juice
- 4 garlic cloves, sliced
- 1 long red chilli, sliced
- 1/2 cup fresh parsley
- 1/2 cup olive oil
- Lemon wedges

Directions

Brush the trout with 2 tablespoons of oil and then place it, skin-side up on a barbecue plate. Cook over the preheated barbecue on high for about 5 minutes and then turn it over. Close the hood and cook on medium heat for another 15 minutes or until cooked through. Transfer to a plate.

In a pan, heat the remaining oil and then sauté garlic until lightly browned. Remove from heat and stir in chilli, and fresh lemon juice; drizzle over the fish and then sprinkle with parsley. Serve garnished with fresh lemon wedges.

Nutrition information per Serving:

Calories: 420; Total Fat: 30 g; Carbs: 1.2 g; Dietary Fiber: trace; Sugars: 1 g; Protein: 37 g; Cholesterol: 111 mg; Sodium: 160 mg

Grilled Chicken Breast with Greek Yogurt

Yield: 3 Servings
Total Time: 2 Hours 10 Minutes
Prep Time: 2 Hours
Cook Time: 10 Minutes

Ingredients

For the Grilled Chicken:

- 3 boneless chicken breast halves, skinned
- 1 clove garlic, minced
- 1 tbsp. lemon juice, freshly squeezed
- 1 tbsp. extra virgin olive oil
- 1 tsp. dried oregano
- Salt and freshly ground black pepper, to taste
- 1 cup plain Greek yogurt, to serve

Directions

Use a sharp knife to gently slice through the thickest part of the chicken breast with cutting all the way through so you are able to open it up like a book. Do this for the other two halves. Marinate the chicken with the remaining chicken ingredients in a large bowl.Cover with cling wrap and set in the fridge for 1 ½ to 2 hours.

Preheat your grill to medium-high heat. Take out the chicken from the marinade. Lightly grease your grill rack then place the breasts on top. Cook for about 3 minutes on each side or until done to desire.

To serve, serve each breast on a large plate. Place a dollop of the Greek yogurt on the side.

Enjoy!

Nutritional Information per Serving:

Calories: 218; Total Fat: 9 g; Carbs: 5.2 g; Dietary Fiber:1.5 g; Protein: 37 g; Cholesterol: 38 mg; Sodium: 368 mg

Red Snapper in Hot Veggie Sauce

Yields: 4 Servings

Total Time:35 Minutes

Prep Time: 15 Minutes

Cook Time: 20 Minutes

Ingredients

- 2 pound red snapper fillets
- ¼ cup canola or extra virgin olive oil
- ½ red bell pepper, chopped
- ½ green bell pepper, chopped
- 4 scallions, thinly sliced
- 2 tomatoes, diced
- 2 cloves garlic
- 2 tablespoons fresh lemon juice
- ½ cup freshly squeezed lime juice
- 1 teaspoon cayenne pepper
- 1 teaspoon pepper

Directions

Add extra virgin olive oil to a skillet and sauté garlic for about 4 minutes or until golden brown. Place fish in the oil and drizzle with lemon and lime juice. Sprinkle with black pepper and cayenne pepper and top with green and red bell peppers, scallions, and tomatoes.

Cover the skillet and simmer for about 15 minutes or until the fish flakes easily with fork.

Nutritional Information per Serving:

Calories: 431; Total Fat: 16.9 g; Carbs: 7 g; Dietary Fiber: 1.9 g; Sugars: 3.7 g; Protein: 61 g; Cholesterol: 107 mg; Sodium: 138 mg

Hot and Spiced Lemon Chicken Thighs

Yield: 4 Servings

Total Time: 55 Minutes

Prep Time: 15 Minutes

Cook Time: 40 Minutes

Ingredients

- 500g chicken thighs
- 2 tablespoons fresh lemon juice
- 1 teaspoon red pepper flakes
- 1 teaspoon sweet paprika
- 1 teaspoon cayenne pepper
- 1 teaspoon freshly ground black pepper
- 1 teaspoon curry powder
- 1 tablespoon garlic powder
- 2 tablespoons coconut oil

Directions

Start by preheating your oven to 400 F and preparing a baking sheet by lining it with parchment paper. Combine all the spices in a small bowl; stir in fresh lemon juice to make a thick paste; then set aside. Now arrange the thighs on your prepared baking sheet with the skin side down (remember to first pat the skin dry with kitchen towels). Rub the upper side of the chicken thighs with half the lemon-seasoning mix, flip them over and rub the lower side with the remaining seasoning mix.

Bake for about 40 minutes until the chicken thighs are cooked through and the skin is crisp. To make the skin crispier, turn on your broiler to high and broil the chicken thighs for 5 minutes.

Enjoy!

Nutritional Information per Serving:

Calories: 281; Total Fat: 13 g; Carbs: 3 g; Dietary Fiber: 1 g; Sugars: 0.6 g; Protein: 36.8 g; Cholesterol: 111 mg; Sodium: 109 mg

Spiced Lemon Baked Tilapia

Yields: 4 Servings

Total Time: 35 Minutes

Prep Time: 15 Minutes

Cook Time: 30 Minutes

Ingredients

- 4 (4 ounce) tilapia fillets
- 4 cloves crushed garlic
- 1 tablespoon minced ginger
- ¼ cup fresh lemon juice
- 1 tablespoon fresh lemon zest
- 3 tablespoons extra-virgin olive oil
- 1 chopped red onion
- 1/4 teaspoon sea salt
- 1/2 teaspoon cayenne pepper
- 4 cups green salad for serving

Directions

Rub the tilapia fillets with garlic and ginger; arrange them in a baking dish. Drizzle the fish with olive oil and lemon juice and sprinkle with lemon zest, cayenne pepper and salt; top with chopped red onion. Refrigerate the fish, covered, for at least 8 hours or overnight to soak in the marinade. When ready, preheat your oven to 175°C (350°F). Transfer the fish fillets to a 9x13 inch baking dish; pour over the marinade mixture and bake the fish for about 30 minutes.

Serve the fish hot with green salad.

Nutritional Information per Serving:

Calories: 194; Total Fat: 11.6g; Carbs: 2.6g; Dietary Fiber: 0.6g; Protein: 21.4g; Cholesterol: 0mg; Sodium: 154mg; sugars: 1.2g

Lemon Garlic Salmon

Yields: 4 Servings

Total Time: 35 Minutes

Prep Time: 15 Minutes

Cook Time: 30 Minutes

Ingredients

- 1 teaspoonextra virgin olive oil
- 4 salmon fillets
- 3 tablespoons freshly squeezed lemon juice
- 1 tablespoon coconut milk
- 1 teaspoon ground pepper
- 1 teaspoon dried parsley flakes
- 1 finely chopped clove garlic

Directions

Preheat your oven to 190°C (275°F). Coat a baking dish with extra virgin olive oil. Rinse the fish under water and pat dry with paper towels. Arrange the fish fillet in the coated baking dish and drizzle with lemon juice and coconut oil. Sprinkle with ground pepper, parsley and garlic. Bake in the oven for about 30 minutes or until the flakes easily when touched with a fork.

Nutritional Information per Serving:

Calories: 248; Total Fat: 12g; Carbs: 0.7g; Dietary Fiber: trace; Protein: 34.8g; Cholesterol: 0mg; Sodium: 82mg; trace

Fried Salmon Fillets with Mashed Potatoes

Yields: 2 Servings

Total Time: 30 Minutes

Prep Time: 10 Minutes

Cook Time: 20 Minutes

Ingredients

- ¼ teaspoon thyme
- ¼ teaspoon basil
- ¼ teaspoon oregano
- ¼ teaspoon onion powder
- 2 teaspoons salt
- ¼ teaspoon white pepper
- ¼ teaspoon ground cayenne pepper
- ¼ teaspoon ground paprika
- 5 ounces tilapia fillet, skin and bones removed
- 2 teaspoons extra virgin olive oil
- 2 servings of mashed potatoes

Directions

Combine oregano, basil, thyme, white pepper, salt, onion powder, cayenne pepper, and paprika in a small bowl.

Brush fish with half of oil and sprinkle with the spice mixture. Drizzle with the remaining oil and cook fish in a skillet set over high heat until blackened and flakes easily with a fork. Serve with mashed potatoes.

Nutritional Information per Serving:

Calories: 188; Total Fat: 6.1 g; Carbs: 19 g; Dietary Fiber: 1.2g; Protein: 15.1 g; Cholesterol: 35 mg; Sodium: 2352 mg; sugars: trace

Spiced Grilled Cod

Yields: 4 Servings

Total Time:35 Minutes

Prep Time: 15 Minutes

Cook Time: 20 Minutes

Ingredients

- 1 pound cod filets
- 2 tablespoon extra-virgin olive oil
- 2 minced garlic cloves
- 1/8 teaspoon cayenne pepper
- 3 tablespoon fresh lime juice
- 1 ½ teaspoon fresh lemon juice
- ¼ cup freshly squeezed orange juice
- 1/3 cup water
- 1 tablespoon chopped fresh thyme
- 2 tablespoon chopped fresh chives

Direction

In a bowl, mix together lemon, lime juice, orange, cayenne pepper, extra virgin olive oil, garlic and water. Place fish in a dish and add the marinade, reserving ¼ cup; marinate in the refrigerator for at least 30 minutes.

Broil or grill the marinated fish for about 4 minutes per side, basting regularly with the marinade.

Serve the grilled fish on a plate and top with the reserved marinade, thyme and chives.

Nutritional Information per Serving:

Calories: 200; Total Fat: 8.1 g; Carbs: 5.5 g; Dietary Fiber: 0.5 g; Sugars: 2 g; Protein: 26.4 g; Cholesterol: 62 mg; Sodium: 91 mg

Spiced Sichuan-Style Prawns

Yield: 4 Servings

Total Time: 30 Minutes

Prep Time: 25 Minutes

Cook Time:5 Minutes

Ingredients

- 450g raw prawns, shelled and de-veined
- 1 spring onion, chopped
- 2 garlic cloves, chopped
- 1 tbsp. minced ginger
- 1½ tbsp. groundnut oil

For the sauce

- 2 tsp. sesame oil
- 2 tsp. Chinese black vinegar
- 3 tsp. chilli bean sauce
- 1 tbsp. tomato purée
- Salt and pepper
- 2 tsp. golden caster sugar
- sliced spring onion
- handful coriander leaves

Directions

Heat groundnut oil in a large pan and then sauté spring onions, garlic and ginger for about 2 minutes or until fragrant; add prawns and stir-fry for 2 minutes. Stir in all sauce ingredients and cook for about 5 minutes. Serve garnished with spring onions and coriander.

Nutritional Information per Serving:

Calories: 156; Total Fat: 6 g; Carbs: 4 g; Dietary Fiber: 0 g; Sugars:3 g; Protein: 20 g; Cholesterol:0 mg; Sodium: 110 mg

Tasty Turkey Chili (Nut-Free, Gluten-Free)

Yield: 1 Servings

Total Time: 35 Minutes

Prep Time: 10 Minutes

Cook Time: 25 Minutes

Ingredients

100g ground turkey

1/2 cup water

6 ounces diced tomatoes

1/2 teaspoon chili powder

1/8 teaspoon cumin

1/8 teaspoon garlic powder

1/8 teaspoon onion powder

Toast

Pinch of sea salt

Pinch of pepper

Directions:

Brown turkey and add all the remaining ingredients; bring to a boil.

Lower heat and simmer for about 20 minutes. Serve with Melba toast.

Freeze extra chili for later use.

Variation: use ground chicken or beef in place of turkey.

Nutritional Information per Serving:

Calories: 245; Total Fat: 12.8 g; Carbs: 19.2 g; Dietary Fiber: 1.6g; Sugars: 3.1 g; Protein: 32.2 g; Cholesterol: 116 mg; Sodium: 580 mg

Grilled Chicken & Green Onion

Yield: 1 Serving

Total Time: 15 Minutes

Prep Time: 10 Minutes

Cook Time: 5 Minutes

Ingredients

3 ounces chicken breast

1 green onion, chopped

Pinch of garlic powder

Pinch of sea salt

Pinch of pepper

Directions:

Place chicken on grill and top with onion slices; sprinkle with garlic powder, salt and pepper and grill for about 5 minutes or until chicken is cooked through.

Nutritional Information per Serving:

Calories: 176; Total Fat: 6.3 g; Carbs: 3.4 g; Dietary Fiber: 0.8 g; Sugars: 1.5 g; Protein: 5 g; Cholesterol: 76 mg; Sodium: 61 mg

SNACKING DRINKS

Ultimate Stomach Elixir

Yield: 2 Servings

Prep Time: 10 Minutes

Ingredients:

- 2 leaves kale
- 2-inch piece of fresh ginger
- 1 apple
- 2 medium carrots
- 1 lemon
- 2 celery stalks
- 1 large beet

Directions

Rinse and peel your ingredients and then slice into pieces; run through the juicer. Serve chilled. Enjoy!

Nutritional info per Serving:

Calories: 131; Total Fat: 0.5 g; Carbs: 32.6 g; Dietary Fiber: 6.7 g; Sugars: 19.7 g; Protein: 2.7 g; Cholesterol: 0 mg; Sodium: 103 mg

Refreshing Citrus Cucumber Juice

Yield: 2 Servings

Prep Time: 10 Minutes

Ingredients

- ½ cucumber, peeled
- 1 orange, halved and peeled
- ½ lemon, peeled
- 1 apple
- 2-inch piece of ginger
- 4 carrots
- 1 tablespoon raw honey

Directions

Rinse the ingredients and juice them all! Stir in a tablespoon of raw honey to sweeten the juice. Serve chilled.

Nutritional info per Serving:

Calories: 205; Total Fat: 0.5 g; Carbs: 52.2 g; Dietary Fiber: 8.9 g; Sugars: 36.6 g; Protein: 3 g; Cholesterol: 0 mg; Sodium: 88 mg

Colon-Loving Green Juice

Yield: 1 Servings

Prep Time: 10 Minutes

Ingredients

- 2 curly kale leaves
- 1 apple
- 2-inch raw ginger root
- 1 teaspoon turmeric
- 1 lemon
- 1 cucumber
- 1 celery stalk
- 1 carrot

Directions

Rinse the ingredients and juice them all! Stir in a tablespoon of raw honey to sweeten the juice. Serve chilled.

Nutritional info per Serving:

Calories: 239; Total Fat: 1.1 g; Carbs: 57.1 g; Dietary Fiber: 9.3 g; Sugars: 23.1 g; Protein: 8 g; Cholesterol: 0 mg; Sodium: 123 mg

Pineapple Aloe Vera Detox Juice

Yield: 2 Servings

Prep Time: 10 Minutes

Ingredients

- 1/2 Aloe Vera leaf
- 1/2 pineapple, cored
- 1/2 lemon
- 1 small cucumber
- 1 cup coconut water

Directions

Wash veggies and fruits.

Slit the edges of aloe vera with a knife to open the outer layer; scoop out the gel and set aside.

Run all ingredients through a juicer and stir in aloe vera gel and coconut water. Serve right away.

Nutritional info per Serving:

Calories: 140; Total Fat: 1 g; Carbs: 33.4 g; Dietary Fiber: 6.1 g; Sugars: 20.1 g; Protein: 4.5 g; Cholesterol: 0 mg; Sodium: 260 mg

Lemon Berry Juice

Yield: 4 Servings

Prep Time: 10 Minutes

Ingredients

- 4 lemons
- 2-inch piece of fresh ginger root
- 1 cup strawberries
- 1 cup raspberries
- 1 cup blueberries
- 1 cup blackberries

Directions

Rinse the ingredients and juice them all! Stir in a tablespoon of raw honey to sweeten the juice. Serve chilled.

Nutritional info per Serving:

Calories: 84; Total Fat: 0.9 g; Carbs: 21.2 g; Dietary Fiber: 7.2 g; Sugars: 10 g; Protein: 2.1 g; Cholesterol: 0 mg; Sodium: 3 mg

Berry Beet Juice

Yield: 2 Servings

Prep Time: 10 Minutes

Ingredients

- 1/2 green apple
- 1 cup blueberries
- 1 cup Swiss chard leaves
- 1 cucumber
- 2 beets, with green leaves
- 2 teaspoons turmeric powder

Directions

Wash all ingredients. Chop veggies and fruits and juice them all. Stir in turmeric powder and enjoy!

Nutritional info per Serving:

Calories: 141; Total Fat: 0.9 g; Carbs: 32.7 g; Dietary Fiber: 1.2 g; Sugars: 20.3 g; Protein: 3.9 g; Cholesterol: 0 mg; Sodium: 199 mg

Refreshing Tomato Celery Juice

Yield: 2 Servings

Prep Time: 10 Minutes

Ingredients

- 1 grapefruit
- 2 oranges
- 2 tomatoes
- 6 medium carrots
- 2 stalks celery

Directions

Wash fruits and veggies. Peel and section grapefruit and oranges. Run everything through a juicer. Serve chilled.

Nutritional info per Serving:

Calories: 207; Total Fat: 0.6 g; Carbs: 50.1 g; Dietary Fiber: 1.4 g; Sugars: 34.1 g; Protein: 4.8 g; Cholesterol: 0 mg; Sodium: 146 mg

Super Body Detoxifier

Yield: 1 Serving

Prep Time: 10 Minutes

Ingredients

- 4 large Swiss chard leaves and stems
- 1-2 inches of ginger
- ½ bunch of organic cilantro
- 1 organic cucumber
- 1 full bunch of organic celery
- 1 lime
- 1 lemon

Directions

Rinse and chop up all ingredients; run them through a juicer and serve.

Nutritional info per Serving:

Calories: 135; Total Fat: 1.4 g; Carbs: 33.4 g; Dietary Fiber: 9.3 g; Sugars: 10.6 g; Protein: 7.2 g; Cholesterol: 0 mg; Sodium: 456 mg

Healthy Berry Juice

Yield: 2 Servings

Prep Time: 10 Minutes

Ingredients

- 2 cups green tea (brewed and chilled)
- 1 1/2 cups blueberries
- 1 1/2 cups raspberries
- 2 cups fresh spinach

Directions

Wash the veggies and fruit. Juice them all and then stir in brewed green tea. Enjoy!

Nutritional info per Serving:

Calories: 117; Total Fat: 1.1 g; Carbs: 27.9 g; Dietary Fiber: 9.3 g; Sugars: 15 g; Protein: 2.8 g; Cholesterol: 0 mg; Sodium: 25 mg

Vegetable Avocado Juice

Yield: 2 Servings

Prep Time: 10 Minutes

Ingredients

- ½ avocado
- 2 cups spinach
- 1 cup purple cabbage
- 2 cucumbers
- 2 lemons
- 1 cup fresh cilantro

Directions

Wash and juice cucumbers, cabbage, lemons and spinach. In a blender, blend the avocado and the vegetable juice until very smooth. Serve right away.

Nutritional Information per Serving:

Calories: 165; Total Fat: 10.5 g; Carbs: 24.1 g; Dietary Fiber: 8.3 g; Sugars: 8.1 g; Protein: 5 g; Cholesterol: 0 mg; Sodium: 5mg

Ginger Pineapple Juice

Yield: 2 Servings

Prep Time: 10 Minutes

Ingredients

- 1-inch slice of fresh ginger
- 1 cup blueberries
- 1 cup diced pineapple
- 4 celery ribs
- 1 cup fresh parsley
- 1 cup mint leaves

Directions

Wash and juice everything. Enjoy!

Nutritional Information per Serving:

Calories: 136; Total Fat: 1.2 g; Carbs: 31.3 g; Dietary Fiber: 8.6 g; Sugars: 16.7 g; Protein: 4.2 g; Cholesterol: 0 mg; Sodium: 97 mg

Spinach Ginger Juice

Yield: 1 Serving

Prep Time: 10 Minutes

Ingredients

- 1-inch slice of ginger
- 1 apple
- 3 carrots
- 1 cup mint leaves
- 1 cup cilantro

Directions

Rinse all the ingredients and run them through a juicer. Serve right away.

Nutritional Information per Serving:

Calories: 121; Total Fat: 0.3 g; Carbs: 29.2 g; Dietary Fiber: 8.3 g; Sugars: 16.3 g; Protein: 2.8 g; Cholesterol: 0 mg; Sodium: 82 mg

Refreshing Pineapple-Ginger Ale

Yield: 2 Servings

Prep Time: 10 Minutes

Ingredients

- 1-inch slice of ginger
- 1 cup diced fresh pineapple
- 1 cup spinach
- 1 cup purple cabbage

Directions

Wash and juice everything. Serve chilled.

Nutritional Information per Serving:

Calories: 57; Total Fat: 0.3 g; Carbs: 14 g; Dietary Fiber: 2.4 g; Sugars: 9.4 g; Protein: 1.4 g; Cholesterol: 0 mg; Sodium: 19 mg

Super Stomach Cleanser Juice

Yield: 1 Serving

Prep Time: 10 Minutes

Ingredients

- ¼ cup fresh aloe vera juice
- 1 lemon, peeled
- 5 asparagus spears
- 1 cucumber
- 1 carrot
- 10 stalks celery
- Handful of cilantro
- Handful of parsley
- Handful of stinging nestle leaves

Directions

Add all ingredients to the juicer and juice. Enjoy!

Nutritional Information per Serving:

Calories: 113; Total Fat: 0.9 g; Carbs: 26.1 g; Dietary Fiber: 8.4 g; Sugars: 11 g; Protein: 6.4 g; Cholesterol: 0 mg; Sodium: 160 mg

Healthy Green Detox Juice

Yield: 1 Serving

Prep Time: 10 Minutes

Ingredients

- 1 medium carrot
- 1 cucumber
- 1 orange, peeled
- 1/2 cup cranberries
- 1 large beet
- Handful of seaweed
- Ice cubes

Directions

Juice everything in a juicer except ice cubes; stir in ice cubes and enjoy!

Nutritional Information per Serving:

Calories: 412; Total Fat: 1.6 g; Carbs: 91.4 g; Dietary Fiber: 18.5 g; Sugars: 64.8 g; Protein: 8 g; Cholesterol: 0 mg; Sodium: 167 mg

Garden Greens Juice

Yield: 2 Servings

Ingredients

- 2-inch piece fresh ginger
- 1 lemon
- 1 green apple
- 4 celery stalks
- 1 cup watercress
- 1 cup seaweed
- 8 romaine leaves
- 1 small bunch of parsley
- 1 small bunch of kale
- 1 small bunch of baby spinach

Directions

Rinse the ingredients and juice them all! Stir in a tablespoon of raw honey to sweeten the juice. Serve chilled.

Nutritional info per Serving:

Calories: 151; Total Fat: 1.5 g; Carbs: 32.6 g; Dietary Fiber: 9.8 g; Sugars: 14.2 g; Protein: 8.3 g; Cholesterol: 0 mg; Sodium: 207 mg

Green Ginger Detoxifier

Yield: 1 Serving

Prep Time: 10 Minutes

Ingredients

- 1 (1-inch) pieces ginger root
- 1 lime, peeled
- 1 orange
- 1 cucumber
- 1 beet
- 2 stalks celery
- 1/2 medium apple

Directions

Add all ingredients to the juicer and juice. Enjoy!

Nutritional Information per Serving:

Calories: 136; Total Fat: 0.8 g; Carbs: 35.5 g; Dietary Fiber: 7.3 g; Sugars: 18.4 g; Protein: 3.8 g; Cholesterol: 0 mg; Sodium: 59 mg

Hot Ginger Citrus Detox Drink

Yield: 2 Servings

Total Time: 2 Minutes

Prep Time: 2 Minutes

Ingredients:

- 2 grapefruit
- 2 oranges
- 2 lemons
- 2 tablespoon apple cider vinegar
- 1 cup hot water
- 1-inch fresh ginger
- 1 dash cayenne pepper
- ¼ teaspoon cinnamon

Directions:

Mix together all ingredients and serve warm.

Nutritional Information per Serving:

Calories: 19; Total Fat: 0.3 g; Carbs: 2.2 g; Dietary Fiber: 0.6 g; Sugars: 0.8 g; Protein: 0.4 g; Cholesterol: 0 mg; Sodium: 15 mg

Green Asparagus Lemon Juice

Yield: 1 Serving

Prep Time: 10 Minutes

Ingredients

- 1 lemon
- A bunch of asparagus
- 2 carrots
- 1-piece ginger
- 4 leaves kale
- 2 stalks celery

Directions

Add all ingredients to the juicer and juice. Enjoy!

Nutritional Information per Serving:

Calories: 294; Total Fat: 1.2 g; Carbs: 76.1 g; Dietary Fiber: 14.6 g; Sugars: 48.4 g; Protein: 4.9 g; Cholesterol: 0 mg; Sodium: 85 mg

Watermelon Green Detox Juice

Yields: 1 serving

Prep Time: 10 Minutes

Ingredients

- 1 cup diced watermelon
- 1 lemon peeled
- 1 cup spinach
- 2-inch knob ginger
- 2 kale leaves
- 1 cucumber, chopped
- 2 celery stalks, chopped
- Handful of fresh parsley or cilantro

Directions

Add all ingredients to the juicer and juice. Serve right away.

Nutritional Information per Serving:

Calories: 158; Total Fat: 1 g; Carbs: 39 g; Dietary Fiber: 9 g; Sugars: 20 g; Protein: 5 g; Cholesterol: 0 mg; Sodium: 112 mg

Hot Healthy Juice

Yield: 1 Serving

Prep Time: 10 Minutes

Ingredients

- 1 cucumber
- 1 lemon
- 2 carrots
- 1 beet
- 1 clove of garlic
- 1 knob ginger
- 1 raw jalapeño pepper

Directions

Rinse and juice all ingredients. Stir and serve right away.

Nutritional info per Serving:

Calories: 171; Total Fat: 0.9 g; Carbs: 41.4 g; Dietary Fiber: 8.7 g; Sugars: 21.1 g; Protein: 5.8 g; Cholesterol: 0 mg; Sodium: 169 mg

Nature's Super Blend Juice

Yield: 2 Servings

Prep Time: 10 Minutes

Ingredients

- ½ medium avocado
- ¼ green bell pepper
- ½ stalk celery
- 2 cups chunk broccoli
- ¼ cucumber
- 2 carrots
- 1 lime
- ¼ zucchini
- 1 handful spinach leaves
- 1 apple
- ice

Directions

Rinse and juice everything, except ice and avocado. Transfer the juice to your blender and add in ice and avocado; blend until very smooth and serve.

Nutritional info per Serving:

Calories: 245; Total Fat: 10.6 g; Carbs: 38.3 g; Dietary Fiber: 11.9 g; Sugars: 18.9 g; Protein: 5.7 g; Cholesterol: 0 mg; Sodium: 96 mg

Stomach Healthy Detox Drink

Yield:1 Serving

Prep Time: 20 Minutes

Ingredients

- 1/8 teaspoon ground turmeric
- 1/8 teaspoon cinnamon
- 1/4 teaspoon cayenne pepper
- 1 teaspoon fresh ginger, chopped
- 1 large lemon, juiced
- 2 tea bags green tea
- 2 cups water
- 1/4 teaspoon raw honey

Directions

In a saucepan set over medium heat, mix water, lemon juice, turmeric, green tea bags, cinnamon, ground cayenne pepper, chopped ginger, and honey.

Bring the mixture to a gentle boil and then simmer for about 5 minutes. pour into mugs and refrigerate for at least 1 hour before serving.

Nutritional info per Serving:

Calories: 32; Total Fat: 0.4 g; Carbs: 8.8 g; Dietary Fiber: 2.2 g; Sugars: 3 g; Protein: 0.9 g; Cholesterol: 0 mg; Sodium: 16 mg

Detox Beet Juice

Yield: 2 Servings

Prep Time: 5 Minutes

Ingredients

- 3 beetroots
- 2 medium apples
- 2 carrots
- 2 oranges, peeled
- 2 lemons, peeled

Directions

Wash and juice everything. Enjoy!

Nutritional info per Serving:

Calories: 310; Total Fat: 1.1 g; Carbs: 78.8 g; Dietary Fiber: 15.9 g; Sugars: 56.8 g; Protein: 6 g; Cholesterol: 0 mg; Sodium: 161 mg

Three-Ingredients Colon Detoxifier

Yield: 1 Serving

Prep Time: 10 Minutes

Ingredients

- 2 slices of pineapple
- 3 large organic celery stalks
- 3 sprigs of parsley

Directions

Wash and juice everything. Enjoy!

Nutritional info per Serving:

Calories: 41; Total Fat: 0.3 g; Carbs: 9.2g; Dietary Fiber: 2.6 g; Sugars: 5.7 g; Protein: 1.1 g; Cholesterol: 0 mg; Sodium: 98 mg

APPENDIX : RECIPES INDEX

Lightning Source UK Ltd.
Milton Keynes UK
UKHW032238180222
398910UK00007B/1550

9 781802 443509